MAKING THE GRADE

Together

EASY POPULAR DUETS FOR YOUNG CLARINETTISTS
SELECTED AND ARRANGED BY LYNDA FRITH

Exclusive distributors:
Music Sales Limited
Newmarket Road, Bury St. Edmunds, Suffolk IP33 3YB.
This book © Copyright 1996 Chester Music.
Order No. CH61175
ISBN 0-7119-5865-3
Cover design by Pemberton & Whitefoord.
Printed in the United Kingdom by
Caligraving Limited, Thetford, Norfolk.

Chester Music

INTRODUCTION

This collection of 16 popular duets has been carefully arranged to provide attractive repertoire for young clarinettists. The technical standard of each part is equal, giving both players an opportunity to play the tune. The pieces are carefully graded, and should be suitable for players using the solo MAKING THE GRADE books 1 to 3.

CONTENTS

THE SOUND OF SILENCE

Words & music by Paul Simon

It is always important to listen to one another in duet playing, and to be aware who has the tune!
Generally allow the player with the main tune to be slightly louder.

UPTOWN GIRL

Words & music by Billy Joel

Be careful with the counting of the rests in this piece.

Sometimes there is a quaver rest at the beginning of a bar, sometimes a crotchet.

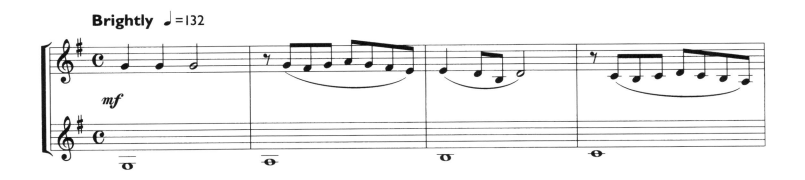

KNOWING ME, KNOWING YOU

Words & music by Benny Andersson, Stig Andersson & Bjorn Ulvaeus

Watch out for the syncopated rhythms! Make sure you don't lose the beat,
especially where the time signature changes in bar 14.

CALIFORNIA DREAMING

Words & music by John Phillips

This is a slow, thoughtful piece of music, with the two parts sometimes moving together,
sometimes independently. Notice the D sharps in bars 15 and 16.

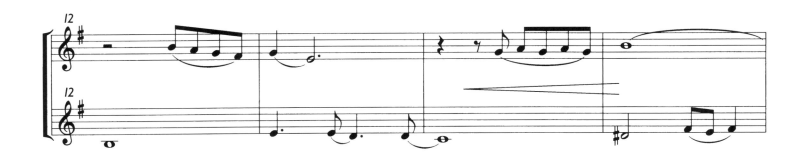

HEARTBEAT

Words & music by Bob Montgomery & Norman Petty

Make sure that the rhythm of the syncopated bars (1, 3, 4, etc.) is counted
very accurately so that you keep in time with one another.

LADY MADONNA

Words & music by John Lennon & Paul McCartney

The chromatic lower part must be tongued firmly to give it a bass-like quality.
Notice the DC al Coda instruction. Go back to the beginning and where it says
'To Coda' jump to the final two Coda bars.

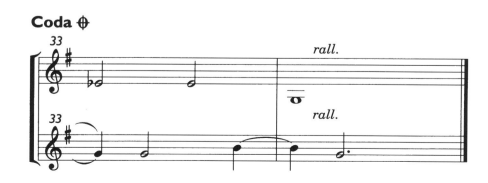

11

DO-RE-MI

Words by Oscar Hammerstein II, music by Richard Rodgers

This simple tune has several accidentals to trip you up!

Choose a player to nod in for the F major scale at the end.

CATHY'S CLOWN

Words & music by Don & Phil Everly

Notice how the two parts have a 'question and answer' interplay.

This is known as antiphonal playing.

CASTLE ON A CLOUD

Music by Claude-Michel Schonberg, lyrics by Herbert Kretzmer
Original Text by Alain Boublil & Jean-Marc Natel

There are many time signature changes in this piece, so keep a steady crotchet pulse throughout.

HAPPY XMAS (WAR IS OVER)

Words & music by John Lennon & Yoko Ono

The parts move very independently in this popular piece.

Try to make the individual phrases rise and fall in volume, to give them shape.

ONE MOMENT IN TIME

Words & music by Albert Hammond & John Bettis

The repetitive rhythm of this piece can sound tedious, so make sure that you observe
the tonguing to avoid stressing the first beat of every bar.

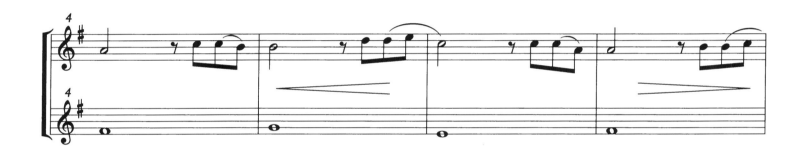

PACHELBEL'S CANON

By Johann Pachelbel

Don't start playing this until you have decided at what speed you can **both** manage the
semiquavers on the second page.

(EVERYTHING I DO) I DO IT FOR YOU

Words by Bryan Adams & Robert John 'Mutt' Lange. music by Michael Kamen

In bars 10, 14, 34 and 38, be especially careful to count the fourth beat before you play the semiquaver.

However, in bars 16, 18, 40 and 42, you must play the semiquaver immediately before the fourth count.

REVIEWING THE SITUATION

Words & music by Lionel Bart

It is important in duets to listen to your partner and to be aware of their music as well as your own.

It is doubly important when the speed of the music varies, as it does in this piece from bar 28.

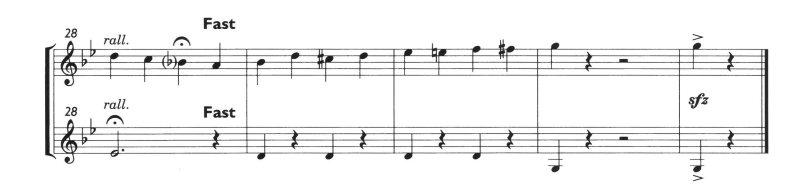

MONEY, MONEY, MONEY

Words & music by Benny Andersson & Bjorn Ulvaeus

Notice the accents in bars 19 and 20. They change from being on the beat to being off the beat.

Don't stop counting!

MACNAMARA'S BAND

Words by John J. Stamford, music by Shamus O'Connor

Notice the counter melody underneath the repeated notes of the tune.